New beginnings

and other writings on being in care

coram
Voice
getting young voices heard

coramBAAF
ADOPTION & FOSTERING ACADEMY

Published by
CoramBAAF Adoption and Fostering Academy
41 Brunswick Square
London WC1N 1AZ
www.corambaaf.org.uk

Coram Academy Limited, registered as a company limited by
guarantee in England and Wales number 9697712, part of the Coram
group, charity number 312278

© The collection CoramBAAF, 2017

British Library Cataloguing in Publication Data
A catalogue record for this book is available from the British Library

ISBN 978 1 9 10039 62 5

Designed and typeset by Helen Joubert Design
Printed in Great Britain by the Lavenham Press
Trade distribution by Turnaround Publisher Services, Unit 3, Olympia
Trading Estate, Coburg Road, London N22 6TZ

About Coram Voice

Children and young people who are vulnerable to harm or exclusion from society, and who have a particular reliance on the state or its agencies for their rights and wellbeing, are far too often not given the support they need. Coram Voice exists to enable and equip those children and young people to express their views in all matters affecting them and have their views taken seriously and therefore improve the system.

We run **Always Heard**, the national advocacy helpline for children in care and care leavers in England, making sure that children in care and care leavers in England get their voices heard.

About Voices

The writings in this book were collected through our writing competition **Voices**.

Voices is a platform for the voices of children in and around the care system. It aims to promote a positive image by showcasing young people's creativity and improving understanding of their experiences, in particular "new beginnings" — what and who have given them opportunities for a fresh start. The national writing competition was launched in 2016 to mark Coram Voice's 40th anniversary and in honour of our founder, Gwen James, who died in 2015. The competition is open to children in care and care leavers.

Voices is an annual competition and Voices 2018 will be open for new entries late 2017. You can find out more through our website www.coramvoice.org.uk.

Acknowledgements

A big thank you to The Queen's Trust, the Hadley Trust, Rosemary and Bernard Mayes, Tim Sharp and Helen Bessemer-Clark and the individual donors whose financial contributions made the Voices competition possible. Thank you to Muna Adams whose inspiration established this competition and individual fundraising allowed us to make the competition a reality.

Thank you to our inspirational judges Jenny Molloy, Paolo Hewitt, Nikesh Shukla, Alex Wheatle, Jackie Long, Keren David, Luke Stevenson, Lisa Cherry, Eleanor Mills, and Richard Grant aka Dreadlockalien.

Thank you to our brilliant hosts, Peter Capaldi and Camelia Borg, for kindly offering their time to join us in celebrating these great young people.

Thank you to all the wonderful volunteers who helped us shortlist the entries and the people across the country who helped promote Voices 2017. Thank you to all the staff across the Coram Group who supported the competition, without whom there would be no Voices 2017. Thanks also go to CoramBAAF for publishing this collection and to the Lavenham Press for donating their printing services.

The biggest thank you of all goes to all the young people who entered this competition and shared their wonderful and unique stories. This publication showcases a selection of the writing submitted, but there were so many more moving and thought-provoking entries. Thank you for showing us how brilliant you really are and for giving us an insight into your perspectives on life, new beginnings and the people who are important to you.

June 2017

Note

Many of the names mentioned in the pieces have been anonymised to protect confidentiality.

CONTENTS

Be inspired!

There are around 70,000 children currently in the care system who, for a variety of reasons, sadly cannot live with their birth parents, sometimes for a short period, sometimes for much longer.

Understanding what that means is hard. But on a most basic level it means that children cannot be with their families, or those they might expect to feel secure and safe with. Instead, they may find themselves dependent upon the support of professionals and strangers often at a most vulnerable and pressurised time of their lives.

The life experiences of these children and young people can be hard for them to recall, make sense of and express.

For many, writing is an effective and therapeutic way of expressing challenging emotions and experiences, as the submissions to Coram Voice's writing competition have revealed, some of which are included in this selection. This rich collection of poetry and prose is a testament to the creativity and remarkable talent of its contributors. They speak of a range of feelings about leaving the familiarity of family and home, starting afresh, dealing with changes, being "lost and found", feeling loved, and what being in care has meant for them.

I had the pleasure of supporting the Voices competition in 2017 and it was a truly inspiring occasion. It is impossible not to be moved and humbled, not only by the creative talent and spirit of resilience of the writers, but also by the courage they display by sharing their personal experiences with the public.

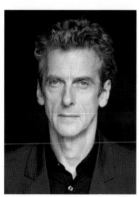

I hope that this selection of entries from the first two Voices competitions will help encourage even more children and young people to share their stories and allow us all to gain a small but powerful understanding into their experience of the care system.

Peter Capaldi

June 2017

What some of the judges say...

I was humbled and honoured to read these poems. Brave young writers are rare and to have been in care myself made the experience a little more real.

Each writer worked hard to capture these words on paper. Coram Voice bound them and published, now it is up to you as the reader to share the messages and emotions afar. Well done. :)

Dreadlockalien

 Dreadlockalien is a poet who grew up in care and became a careleavers' advocate for Voice. He was Birmingham Poet Laureate in 2005/6, met the Queen in 2013 at an event for British contemporary poetry, hosts BBC Radio 4's slam poetry show and Glastonbury Poetry and Words, and is a judge for the Young Muslim Writers Awards.

To be given permission to look at the world through the eyes of the young writers in the Coram Voice writing competition is an absolute privilege. The world the young people show us through their narratives is one of hope, strength and opportunity. Life in care does not have to be a negative, and this was powerfully illustrated throughout the text. I remember so many of the submissions with joy in my heart and acknowledge the talent that sits within children and young people who have experienced childhoods that they simply do not deserve. Even with the hurt and pain that goes with those childhoods, children and young people teach us with such courage that they are more than their past and that this pain does not have to define their future.

The submissions brought out a variety of thoughts and feelings in me, with some making me laugh — real belly laughs where tears are streaming and you are holding your tummy as it's aching with laughter pains — and some making me remember the same feelings I had when I was in care, which gave me a real pause for thought about how lucky we all are to have a social care system that places children at the heart of all it tries to do.

Social workers and teachers emerged as significant and important to the young people. With bravery, they rejected the common perception that as children in care we do not like or wish to spend time with our special adults. The desire to feel protected and safe in their worlds dominated the children and young people's writing and gave a sense of their needing to be able to participate in decisions that are made about them. Friendships were equally as important and the happiness that those friendships brought into the children's lives was beautiful to be able to read.

Thank you to all of the children and young people who submitted their writing and gave me permission to share a little part of their lives.

Jenny Molloy

 Jenny Molloy spent most of her childhood in care. She regularly gives talks and advises government bodies on the care and fostering of children. Jenny is the successful co-author of *Hackney Child* and *Tainted Love* under her pen name Hope Daniels, and *Neglected*, her first title under her real name. She is a Patron of BASW England and a regular contributor to *Community Care*.

I have only ever reported on life in care. I have never lived it. So I am not — and would never claim to be — an expert. But something that strikes me whenever I speak to a young person living in care is that making their voice heard is often too difficult — sometimes impossible. The loneliness of that always seems unfair. To have a story to tell and yet sometimes have no one to hear it.

The great pleasure of judging the Coram Voices writing competition was hearing young people making their voices heard, loud and clear, and beautifully too!

Each piece was different, strikingly so but that's because every voice sounds different, every story twists and turns in its own unique way. Here we have pieces that are musical, lyrical, while others are much more straightforward in their storytelling. All of them are a joy to read. We hear sadness, but also strength and resilience and optimism.

I could, and am sorely tempted to, quote lines from each piece that stand out but instead I will leave it for you to read and enjoy yourselves! It was my privilege to read them first – I hope you get as much out of the work as I did.

Jackie Long

Jackie Long is the social affairs editor and presenter for *Channel 4 News*. She joined the programme in 2011, following more than two decades at the BBC. Most recently, she was Correspondent at *Newsnight*, and she previously worked on *The World at One*, *PM* and *Five Live*.

PART 1
Finding a new life

My very own

Kai, age 15

I was trembling in my little shoes, I didn't know what to do!
My mum bellowed 'I love you!'
My heart felt a horrible stabbing pain.
Will I ever have a family who loves me again?
I was given to a couple who wanted me for me.
To them it is not a job to get done,
But to be my loving parents and me their son.
From the darkness I began to shine,
And in my heart I held a family which is mine.
All the thoughts of the past did not everlast.
Now me and my sister have got a family who loves us a lot
And all the pains of the past burned and forgot.
I no longer want them thoughts to make me sad,
And guiding me all the way is my very own
Mam and dad.

A new chapter

Georgia, age 20

Coming into care at the age of fourteen
It's not a nice feeling when you're being escorted
To a family that's not been specified
All you want to do is sit and hide
No place to go, no one familiar in your home
Start of my first chapter in care

After many moves I was so confused
Nothing seemed to be going right
I couldn't sleep at night
The placements breaking down
Falling to the ground
The pain in my heart
No hope left scars marked
One last move my last chance
Look so scary at first glance

One January afternoon twenty fourteen
A new chapter in my book a new beginning
A different place I'd never been
Strangers all around
People making sounds
Not used to this
I'm out of my place
Don't know what to do
Don't know what to say
Feeling like a rabbit in headlights
So bright under the spotlight

I met a nice lady my key worker to be
She was kind and so funny
We talked about life and what I liked
From football to art and writing music too
We shared an interest did something new

She settled my nerves made me feel at ease
Two years later I've moved out
And she's there at a shout

This new beginning changed my life
I'm so much stronger
I've had to fight
The monsters at night
But this is my life
I'm the one who's going to strive

The past is in the past the future is near
I'm not gunna shed a tear
Starting from the bottom
Now aiming for top
Music is my life writing nonstop
People say care kids amount to nothing
But I'm going to prove them wrong,
I'm going to be something
Working hard being strong
Fresh start I can be me
I'm going to get this uni degree

A smile on my face
I'm in a better place
Bad pasts and the scars do last
Being you is the best you can be
Don't change for anybody you are you
we all have equality.

Hidden in the shadows

Shanika, age 12

Lost little girl,
Hidden in the shadows,
Sat in the darkest corner of the room.
Day after day,
Shaking with fear.
Banging on the door,
Shouting in the night,
Tossing and turning
On the cold, dusty floor.
She wishes for the life of the girl
On the front cover of 'OK' magazine.
Who probably doesn't realise how lucky she is.
It's the life the little girl will never have.

So she thinks . . .
The next day a lady awaits her,
In the office at school –
'Oh no' she thinks.
How wrong could she have been.
Veronica was her guardian angel,
She was about to change her life,
For the first time someone had listened.
She didn't like her new 'parents'.
What was she even to call them?
The little girl was lost.
She'd had no childhood.
She'd lock herself in her,
Shut everyone else out.

However,
Nobody gave up on her.
They worked hard.

In time they fought off her demons.
She was happy,
She played,
She laughed and smiled.
The lost little girl
Had come out of the shadows,
Led by the light of her guardian angels.
Her new family.
They'd given her a home,
A life,
A future,
A childhood and
Best of all, a family.
All things she'd never had before.
For that,
She could never thank them enough.
Never give up hope,
The girl once hidden in the shadows,
Has proven to be so much more!

My life story

Callum, age 15

Yeah it all started when me and my fam parted
They said it wasn't my fault
But there was a part of me that knew it was
I didn't have the guts to stand up to the heads
so I kept my head down and at the right time went to bed

But then s*** went dead I started walking away from the rules
they put there
Got kicked out of schools and homes and in time I didn't care
I didn't show no fear
Hood up tunes on walking round the streets either that or on a
BMX
Trying to run and find beef I didn't call my sen a thief
But whenever someone was happy I did my best to crease
ye it was stupid of me cos I tried to take that away
I guess they had what I didn't so it was an emotion in a way

I went to this place i guess my heart was pounding
cos that's the 9th place I've been to I was unsure when they
wasn't shouting
Cos I was used to b***** 24/7 Shouting and arguing I guess this
place was heaven

They took me in fed me bought me clothes talked to me when I
was down
Tried to help me in the way that I needed
and sed 'we will always be around and we are here when you
need us'
I knew at that time I wasn't leaving I started believing
not just in me but the future I could be leading

All thanks to them in side I'm not bleeding

These lyrics that you're listening to
Is my life story that I'm reading
So listen up life's not all bad
Of course missed my dad
but I know he's proud and happy with the life I've had
It may not have been all good but it's not been all bad
I'm starting to change and I wish sooner that I would have
but this is my time and I know they are gonna continue to help
me out
Thanks Mel and Brian I hope I make you proud.

My first match

Jamie, age 9

I wrote my poem/rap about my first footy match for ****
United under 10s. My foster carer takes me to all the training and
matches and stands in the cold every Saturday morning. And she
washes my kit.

My first match,
My breath I can't catch,
A hug to relax,
She helps me chillax,

Changing room disorder,
She's my best supporter,
Coach going mad like he oughta,
Gonna win – we gotta.

I'm part of a team,
My teams in Green,
Strip of white in between,
She washed it clean,

Out on the pitch,
Out positions fixed,
Opposite our enemies,
Same as us – different identities.

Kick off whistle,
The game on – it's official,
She supports me – It's that simple,
Kick pass header dribble,

Cheeky pass forward,
Defender wrong footed,
Change to press onward,
Perfect cross booted.

Header in muddy midfield,
Feet should be four wheeled,
A space is revealed,
Mud heavy and congealed

The space is gaping,
Balls mine for the taking,
Legs are aching,
Crowd is baiting.

Four strides to the keeper,
Feels like a hundred meters,
Direct kick or a faker,
Knick now or later,

I'm rocking new Nikes,
Goalie trying to psych me,
Wanna tackle – try me,
Bang – top bins – bite me,

She's the loudest in the crowd,
Cheering me on proud,
Goal allowed,
I dabbed and bowed,
Man of the match I am crowned!

New school

Queenie, age 14

A chance to start afresh, somewhere where no one knows you.
Unknown. A beautiful yet terrifying
word. I step through the gates wearing the same uniform as
everyone else, identical. Yet somehow I
stand out. I am unknown. I attract a few stares, a few warm
smiles. I keep my head down and turn
my music up. My expression stays blank. I walk wherever my feet
take me, I have no Idea where I'm
going or where I should be going but it would be fatal to stop
now. I look up and see a sign.

'Reception', it says. I follow the sign and smile at the kind looking
woman sitting behind the desk.
'I'm new', I inform her. As if it wasn't obvious already. She takes
my name and year group and
instructs me to take a seat. I sit, waiting.

Waiting for my new beginning to start.

Half an hour later I have had a brief tour of the school, seen my
new timetable and been escorted to
my first lesson. English. I sit at my desk pretending not to notice
the curious stares burning into my
back. I focus on my new English teacher. She is young, cheery,
energetic and funny. My favourite
kind of teacher. I lose myself in her words, she is talking about
Shakespeare. Not my favourite but
she manages to make it interesting enough.

I am not so lucky next period. Maths. I hate maths. I may not be bad at it, but I hate it. The teacher seems nice though. I look for an empty seat and sit in the first one I find. I return the kind smiles of the girls at my table and look down at my empty new book. Maybe this won't be so bad. It's what I wanted isn't it?

My new beginning.

The gentle breeze

Jack, age 17

The gentle breeze of wind scurried over my back as I awoke to a new day. I breathed a soft sigh as I
collected my thoughts, each word travelling around my brain like a hurricane. I had been warned so I
knew what to expect. I got up and put on my pyjamas and tip-toed downstairs where I noticed the
letter on the sofa, it was a warning that I could be taken away from my home. Most children would
be scared, maybe cry, but I had to be strong.

As I poured my drink and set it on the table I thought of the events that had led to this point; the few
disasters that would change my life. The first and most important disaster was when my mother
went into debt; she was happy to admit it was her fault but she still knew that life was about to get
tough. We went from being a fairly normal family who lived off high brand food to being a family
scrounging for even the smallest benefits. Long story short; my mother broke, she understood that
she couldn't care for me like this and made the hardest choice of her life.

I still think about that call she made. Since we lived in a small house I heard every word from her
mouth, I could even make out some of the words on the other end of the phone. It was obvious that
it was the police with the typical voice. "This is the state department, what's your emergency" and
all that scripted rubbish.

My mother cried and pleaded that they help me, take me somewhere
where I could live happily again. I cried too. I cried all night, not because I felt unwanted but because
I knew my mum was doing the right thing.
Not long after I was greeted at the door by a social worker who had to take me to my new home, she
was very cheerful, which helped bring my already low mood up. She explained how the next few
weeks of my life would go and what would happen, all of which I was fine with, and stopped the car
outside of a small, but very cosy, house.
'Don't worry' she told me with a glint of joy in her eyes as she knocked on the door. A man
answered, quite old but seemingly pleasant, he too gave off a feeling or cheeriness. He showed me
to my room and left again to talk to the social worker while I laid out my things and placed them
where needed. I found a picture of my mother and I and clutched it against my chest as I laid down
and closed my eyes.
I finished my story with a strong smile as I looked into the eyes of my new carers of just over a year,
it had taken a long time to be comfortable enough to tell them, but now, it feels like home.

Palace bound

Allie, age 14

I lay alone in an incubator box,
Poisoned.
My body twisted – stiff.
I didn't understand
This world of pain
in which I was set adrift.

Until I was scooped up –
In arms that love me.
That held me in – tight and warm.
That made my pain more bearable.
That gave me hope in being born.

I walked alone,
In the 'play'ground.
Trying desperately to catch someone's eye;
Trying eagerly to be 'part of' it;
Trying fiercely not to cry.

Until I was scooped up –
In arms that love me.
That took me out of school.
And they told me that I AM good enough.
That my classroom can be at home.
And I am learning to learn again,
And becoming smiley-whole.

I sat alone
In my bedroom.
Battered, shocked and hurt.
Trying not to think about WHO
did this to me.
Why? How could they be so monster-cruel?

Until I was scooped up,
In arms that love me.
That held me safe and tight.
That never left me
Day or night.
And they stood up and by and for me;
And they went to court and fought –
And won. 🎁

Now I am alive again.
Those memories will no longer beat me down.
I am a Royal Princess Palace-bound.
New beginnings are paved before me
And truly, completely – at least for now –
I am ME again.
Look! I'm wearing my happiness crown!

Change

Eli, age 13

Change is not always a choice
It makes you nervous and upset
And sometimes you lose control
Where is my voice?
Where is my Mum?

Change is not always a choice
New beginnings might be hard
Things will be different
That's not fair
Where is my voice?
Where is my Mum?

Change is not always a choice
You might be scared at first
There's lots of questions
That can make you dizzy
But I have a voice
And I have a Mum

Change is not always a choice
But, you'll get used to it
And things will get easier...
I have a voice
I have a Mum.

New beginnings

Callum, age 11

Never trust your mums, they say they will but they don't
Ensure you listen carefully and follow the rules, or you will get
    seriously hurt
When you're good you are promised a treat, but it never happens

Before I left I gave them all a cuddle. I said I would never forget
    them.
Everyone I know has gone. Everywhere I look is strange.
Give up thinking about your family, they are never gonna come
    back
I love my family and it's really hard not being with them
Nevertheless, now I've got my new family but I'll never forget
Now it's time to move on again. I had so much fun ....
I'm not moving schools. I'm so glad I've still got my friends and
    teachers
Now I'm with my new carers. I will never forget them
Gillian and Robert are fun. I've been everywhere and seen so
    much
Such love and happiness to take with me to my long term carers

My daily reprise

James, age 15

I bled the bed
And miscarried my dreams
And now flutter on bird wings
And ride on other flighty themes
Waiting
For the signal
To set me free

And then suddenly

A juvenile cacophony
Blares
As I emotion-
lessly. Freeze.

And subsequently
Descend to never land on my feet

And lurch past Neverland
Where the freaks, like me, will never leave
And I see that girl, my friend
Who had always sought to be believed
Who they claimed was mentally diseased

One day I'll learn that they meant totally
Deceased

But her grin is grand and she seems happy

And I yearn for the freedom

Her smile deceives

And grieve

And collide with cold air

As down I go
Let down by the people who claim to love
Me so

And
start
to
  spiral
    out of
control
Then waxy wings are set upon me

But flames too
By the same people who
Claim they'll help me through

This flight
My 'self-imposed' plight

And below me, hell is vividly alight
Just as I was told by mummy and daddy
And their faces stir up from the flames to
haunt me

And the menacing sound matures

And I'm faced with new chores

But
        then
        your silhouette
     It starts to pirouette
        Glide slick to a gold sunset
        You're
        Why
I
No
Longer
Fret

And I alight
You hold me upright
Just before my concrete flight
And I'm saved from my Icarus demise
And go on to suffer from life

Though tonight:

     Please don't say a word if you hear my cries
     Just be there to dance
        With me as the sun shies
        And the moon shines

I've learned to love
     My daily reprise.

Being me!

Connor, age 9

My family made me. They made what I am today.

WHO ARE MY FAMILY?

My mum:
My mum gave birth to me. She is very kind and helped make part of who I am today, she made choices which got us separated. My mum was an alcoholic who is still drinking wine but not as often as before. She was a blonde haired woman, who still sees me today. She lied to the school saying I was ill when I didn't want to go to school. She let me play on Xbox all day and night which she shouldn't have done.

My dad:
I've never met my dad before but I know he was Jamaican and an intelligent man.

Mummy C & Daddy T:
I met my Mummy C & Daddy T when I was 7. They helped me apply for a grammar school which I appreciate a lot. They let me do a lot of clubs like: Football (I support Manchester United), rugby, cricket, band practice, tutoring, drums, clarinet, gardening and swimming. They support me throughout games and tests. Mummy C & Daddy T have really been a big hit in my life. They even set house rules that kept me safe.
· No violence
· Listen to people
· Sharing

They treat me like a gold coin! They take me to theme parks.

YOU WOULD BE REALLY LUCKY TO HAVE PARENTS LIKE
MUMMY C & DADDY T!

My brother D:
D came to live with us a few months ago. We really enjoy spending
time together playing on the PlayStation 3 and playing games. Even
though me and D still have fallouts we are normally friends again the
next day.

My brother M:
I met M when I arrived. He lets me play with him a lot. He is kind and
polite and helpful he's helped me practice my sports to help me get
better.

These are the people who helped make me ME!

THE PROS IN FOSTER CARE

You get treated fairly and kindly by your foster parents but to me they
are just like having another pair of actual parents. You get to go: On
days out, sleepovers, gatherings and to meet and play games together.
We really enjoy it and we even learn to trust people and to learn
social skills.

HERE IS A STORY FROM LAST YEAR

One day at Marbledale we were doing a high trapeze and Mummy C
helped me to jump, Mummy C got nervous when it was her turn she
didn't want to do it. The people there cheered her up the ladder and
finally she got to the top and didn't want to jump off. Then I shouted
out to Mummy C 'I've got faith in you Mummy C' whilst holding the
rope. She said that made her jump as she trusted me when I held the
rope then she jumped off into thin air, we did it as a team.

And from that day on me and Mummy C have always had a trust
between us.

My heroes...
My happiness...

Steven, age 14

I lay there like death lies over the graves of the living. Jumping into the darkness of the night like light jumps into the darkness of the abyss. My life being shadowed like the British clouds shadow the light and all that is good for this world. Being drowned into the depths of the ocean like a fish gets drowned in the depths of the air. My soul being burnt like the rain burns the fire to the deepest pits of hell. But still I am happy, and the two people who make this possible, Sean and Deborah.

When all feels wrong in the world I think of them and all is correct again. In this world of war and torment I think of them how much I love them and how they have helped me throughout my life. They are my real parents and I love them with all of my heart. I have been with them for 10 years. now and when I think of them I think of my heroes...
Before I met these amazing people I was on a rollercoaster but now I am on a rollercoaster that now can only go up. I felt like hell was on my heart but then I was opened up to love again. I felt suddenly like there was a huge weight on my two shoulders and then I met these two people the weight was suddenly lifted. The only two people who were solely responsible for this. My heroes... Sean and Deborah...

I had felt a new emotion that I had never felt before. I was greeted by happiness. I was greeted by another feeling that I had never felt before when I met them... love. My eyes filled with tears of joy as I struggled to keep in the happiness. Warmness flooding through my veins. A sigh of relief as I felt as though I had found my safe haven...

Struggling to control my emotions as strangers became my friends and friends became my family. Could I have been there? Was I in heaven? Every day I asked myself these exact same questions. But then I have to come back into reality and realise that I was still in this same world of war and torment. But with these people helping me through my poisonous life I can do it and I will eventually become stronger and no longer crying my way to sleep every night...

My soul had been torn apart but now it has been sewn back together... by my heroes...

The past ten years of my life have been the best I have ever experienced. Our family is like the story of Romeo and Juliet except in our family the love is returned because there is always love and sometimes it is consistent and that is why I love my family and they love me in my family. They are my heroes. They are my happiness. I love them loads...

Meadfoot Beach

Jena, age 16

As I step onto the sand, I inhale the sweet, salty air and feel it rush into my lungs. I smile at the sheer freshness of it as if feels like a soft blanket creating a sense of calm and happiness into the very depths of my heart.
I look to my right and smile up at my Dad, who grins back with his sea-blue eyes and the joy-worn crinkles around his jovial face.
I look past my Dad at Shannon and watched as her red hair blew in the wind and her beauty strikes me as her face lights up as he looks into the horizon before us.
My big brother Mitchell grabs my hand and we look at each other and laugh as we all hold hands and make our way onto the soft, golden sand crunching beneath our feet and between our toes.
My two dogs, Dillon and Troy, run along the shoreline at a slow and relaxed run. I watch as the sun reflects off their fluffy coats; it makes the brown on their fur turn to a soft and shining gold as the setting sun casts a glow onto the beach and the blue glistening sea.

Its moments like this when I could just freeze time and relive the moment forever. I have never felt so much happiness than when I'm with my family. I love their affectionate glances and smiles and the way my Brother changes into a completely different person when we're with Dad; we never fight and can just be together, loving each other, and laughing without the normal everyday struggles. I love my Dad and Shannon and I'm so glad they found each other because when they are happy, so am I. We stand together with the water sloshing at our feet, staring at the golden glow of the setting sun and I smile.

I learnt to swim

Amy-Jo, age 17

The wet October nights were desolate, drenching and
demoralising.
I wandered the streets in a naive attempt to rest my head, this
cold, wet bench was my bed.

I was learning the skills of this urban jungle.
Learning to show no fear.
                no trust.
                no love.
All of these were eroded away with the rain of each passing day.

Nothing could prepare me for the coldness of them nights.
I could not differentiate between this numbing, blistering wind
and the numbness that lay within my core as a void.
An abyss of emptiness.
Something was missing.
Someone was missing.

I was reborn that November.
Given the warm blanket of their unconditional love.
Given a cup of tea with two lumps of understanding and
acceptance.

You see, water doesn't have to be grey and imposing like that
October rain.
It can be blue,
        purifying
and truly beautiful.

I realise this because I learnt to swim this year.

My swimming abilities are a symbol of pulling through to the other side.
Because the hardest part of swimming is overcoming the fear of drowning.
But now I have that secure base.
I have people that will lift my head and spirit high above the water.
Now I don't have to be scared of the world.
Once I came to this realisation I could see the world's true beauty.
You see, there is a misconception that it is harder to learn new skills as you age.
But this is only because you become fearful and cynical of the world around you. But this doesn't have to be the case.
Nobody has to be hardened by their past to a point of no return.
I believe there is a child in all of us trying to get out.
Curiously and courageously seeking adventure.

Swimming wasn't my new skill, learning to be open minded and open hearted was.

The people that gave me that warm blanket and tea have given so much more in the past three years that I have known them.

They have created my new beginning.
Just as I have created their new beginning.

PART 2
Moving on

Katie

Helen, age 18

When my path seemed bleak
and torn,
all hope lost,
and I felt so worn,

You gave me hope.

When I felt most alone,
With nowhere to turn,
When the light had died away,
From the fire that used to burn,

You gave me courage.

When all seemed futile,
and the prospects grim,
When my courage was lowest,
and my belief so slim,

You gave me light.

The type of hope,
That burns and ignites,
Hope that burns,
and sets your heart alight.

You gave me courage,
To face those fears.
Fight the monsters I had hid from,
All these years.

You gave me a light,
Cast upon my face.
A new-found hope,
I thought could never be the case.

But your light and belief,
I thought could never last,
My thoughts were haunted,
By the memories of my past.

Memories of the people,
Who would come and go.
Their seeds of mistrust,
Planted had begun to grow.

But you never gave up on me.

More and more I felt you were true,
That you truly believed all the things you said I could do.

From the very first night,
When you stayed up to listen to me,
To all those times you never judged,
As my tears fell free.

You meant so much so quickly,
and quickly chased the doubt,
You showed me the trust,
That I had always gone without.
And even when I get scared,

and my head is awful fearful,
Even when I question everything,
and I can't help being tearful.

You've stood by me reassuringly,
Reminded me I can win this fight,
You've reminded me how far I've come,
And you continue to offer me that guiding light.

You are the one place I feel safest,
The one person I know,
Will never harm me,
No matter where life sees us go.

Each hurdle I face,
On the path I now choose,
With you in my life,
I know I will not lose.

Bright ahead
past way behind

Charlotte, age 12

Already in my room but my years heard their muffled words,
Lies from that carer, on who was downstairs.
Told to be quiet and return back to my room.
But why, I don't want to, but no-one listened.

Thankfully it turned out the voice meant I was to be moved on.
Random journey with Social Worker, radio playing out.
Freaky conversation about a dead child,
that the cruel woman who called herself Mum had lost.

Saw my new placement, wow like a mansion.
Wait, steady, calm down, deep breaths.
Walk over, doors open, floating smells of food.
Two people smiling something I'm not used.

COULD THIS BE IT, A HOME.

Days into weeks into months, trust grows, fun begins, laughter heard.
Back with my sister and brother, they giggle, they eat, we cuddle here.
This is where it starts this is where I want it to end.

HERE AS A FAMILY

The life of a girl who has been here a short time but in her heart
a life time.
A lost girl, a found girl, a girl with a life now.
New start, reborn at seven years two months,
No worry about that, just different, no need to explain.
Just a future, hope, acceptance, a world to meet,
Yes a life to greet and live for, the reason to go on.
I'm looking forward!

My advocate

Annabel, age 23

Dedication far beyond expectation
loyalty and familiarity
An advocate, fan, support or crutch
whichever you want to call her
she was far beyond my expectations.

Being there to hear me cry
To hold me when the pain got too much
Someone to care when all became dark
Someone to talk to when all else became silent
A voice a Coram voice.
Those dark days brightened by her visits
every time bringing me a present
Only a pen but a pen none the less.

She brought smiles, light and joy
She brought hope
She brought life.

My advocate gave me a voice,
life and the will to go on.

So the meaning of life;
is to have a voice
to have a point
to feel wanted
to feel cared for
and all those things can be fulfilled
and achieved with a little bit of help from
My advocate
And that's what she did for me.

Pursuing my dreams

Ahmed, age 18

A young teenager, with no understanding of English language, enrolled himself at ***** College at age 16; what he could speak was only (hello, hi, and how are you); nothing else. He was interested, enthusiastic, and passionate in education and wanted to widen his knowledge, but the fate and bad situation in his home country took the entire opportunity from him.

That young teenager is me whose unknown destiny drove him here in the UK. When I arrived from a war torn country to a developed country, it was extremely tough to find my feet but my teachers and key worker supported me to avert my feeling of being in a foreign country; that there is no place for me, as a young migrant.

For a while everything was tough as you could imagine, from social isolation to the language barrier and indecisive. The life was going on with dullness; I neither had the courage to speak with someone nor was daring enough to make friends. As a result of the language barrier, I was feeling isolated most of the time in the college and lacked confidence. Most of my class peers were fluent in speaking the language. I had to motivate myself, but it was not working. I was overwhelmed by difficulties. Let me describe it in one word that is Miserable! My teachers always encouraged and inspired me by their motivating, powerful and wonderful words; as always my key worker does. They advised me not allow the word (I can't) in your vocabulary.

With my thinking, things started to change. I convinced myself that I had to learn the language, as I didn't like to be dependent to someone else. I began listening to news, English podcasts, music, reading daily newspaper, attending college regularly on time, going to English speaking club and many others activities to drag myself out of this situation; as all of them paid off.

One thing I love about this country is that there are opportunities available for everyone to pursue their lofty dreams and to choose their career in any field they wish to. I found people absolutely nice and friendly, contrary to my earlier doubts if there were lovely and kind people still existed and that gave me hope for humanity.

I'm delighted to tell you that my efforts have started to follow my dreams and I have achieved what looked impossible a year ago; to be the student president at ***** College, passed my course with good grades. Achievements inspire me to work hard towards my future goals. A substantial credit of my success goes to the support of my friends, teachers and my key worker.

Thank you

Stevie, age 21

My rap about my experience in the care system and finding my forever family

Seventeen placements.
Too many places.
Too many faces.
I was lost in a maze till my seventeenth placement.
I moved to North West.
But it weren't like the rest.
I felt accepted.
After years of rejection.
I really fitted in.
I learnt to deal with my emotions and take it on the chin.

I bought her cards on Mother's Day.
She pulled me back when I was led astray.
She was there for me through everything.
And helped me move on to better things.
Single carer she was like my mum & dad.
The family I never had.
I stayed long term and turned my life around.
My foster mum deserves a crown.

This is my forever family.
And this is my thank you.

My life

Clara, age 19

I was never born to live in one place,
My life so far
Has been an unexpected adventure
New places;
New people;
New cultures.

I always have to adapt,
Sometimes I don't fit in
Because people don't understand where I have come from
But sometimes, I find people like me
And we bond.
We share our experiences
We laugh and
We cry.

Sometimes I wonder
How it feels to grow up in one place with the same people
Will I feel part of something?
That I will never know.
My life consists of new beginnings.

I know what it's like to be a butterfly

Natasha, age 24

I know what it's like to be a butterfly... the world is large and overwhelming. Not being sure where you fit in and how such a fragile and exposed creature can protect and provide for itself, amongst the darkness and the rain that falls. To be aware that one drop of rain can kill a butterfly; having to be strong in the face of danger, yet showing beauty and elegance and everyone around the butterfly feels love, not realising the real feelings or emotions the butterfly goes through every day to survive.

The butterfly being so small and delicate they are under constant threat from predators that will kill them. Not being able to escape the chase from the creature that has decided to attach its vision to the luminescent colours that reflect and beam from the butterfly's wings, which makes the butterfly beautifully vulnerable. the butterfly seems to dip in and out of the air so easily almost as if there is such powerful control in such an innocent being that you can't recognise how much effort the butterfly puts in to stay floating in the air...

But a butterfly does not start out as a butterfly. The butterfly had changed.

Before the butterfly had changed it was a caterpillar. The caterpillar that started out was greedy and selfish and although still vulnerable to other predators, the caterpillar seemed safer than the butterfly. The caterpillar was able to hide and close the world around itself away, finding solace in the silence and the darkness. The caterpillar was not damaged or killed by rain;

the caterpillar just kept eating and eating, getting larger and larger and gluttonizing itself with contentment and sometimes misery. After a while the caterpillar changed. It took a very long time and the caterpillar became slow and even more delicate to danger. The caterpillar surrounded itself with the walls of its cocoon and hibernated in silence. No one to protect the vulnerability of the caterpillar anymore... the caterpillar was changing and it was changing alone. For what seemed like forever soon ended and the walls of the cocoon opened allowing the transformation of the caterpillar to the butterfly. What the caterpillar longed for was freedom, but when the caterpillar had become the butterfly, freedom was no longer desired and all the butterfly wanted and needed was protection and love...

I know what it's like to be a butterfly, I also know what it's like to be a caterpillar, and how so much change can affect even the smallest things in life, and can change the beautiful into the broken and the tough into the weak. The longing and desires of change, but never being able to protect yourself within the change. The being alone due to greed, selfishness and lack of emotion; to the longing for one person to let you know they will be there and protect you through the scariest and most dangerous times in your journey of life, but never quite making it to that person before the rain starts falling and you could potentially die. I know I have been the caterpillar many times and I have been cocooned many more times, and every now and again I am the butterfly. I wish there was another adaption to the butterfly who could fend for itself and never be the prey or the predator to others, just something strong and independent, powerful but majestic in beauty and seeing the beauty that it could share with others, the rain not damaging or killing it. Just being able to overcome the alone, the silence and the fragile to being one thing... Me!

Bruce

Annabel, age 23

His gentle nature, smooth chestnut fur drew me to him. His eyes had a deep warm feeling. He was caring, he knew how pain felt and wanted to rescue me. It was immediate. The feeling when I first set eyes on him was overwhelming. This tall handsome horse in front of me was to change my life. Every minor improvement built into a major step forward. He walked towards me head bent, we came closer slowly, instantly I felt safe. He rubbed his head on me, invading my space but not making me fearful. I was at peace. How could such a large animal project such a gentle secure feeling? That's Bruce for you.

Butterflies in my stomach but with a calm aura. I set out to take my first ride on Bruce. I tentatively approached him slipping his head collar on; he gave me an affectionate snort and instantly put me at rest. I walked him slowly towards the block, his large hoofs teetering along. He had poorly feet. He understood pain. Gently I coaxed this giant over the cobbles tacking him up, preparing myself for my mount. As a climbed on he stayed very still, he reassured me that he would be my protector. This first riding encounter was to be the beginning of an amazing journey.

Ever since that first meeting Bruce has brought calm to my life. He encouraged me to speak openly whilst keeping me safe and calm. As I lay on his back I can feel his love seep through me. His ears listen tentatively to my every word, obediently following my every command.

I didn't ride Bruce I was Bruce. Never once when I sat upon Bruce's back did I feel I was his rider. I was always part of him I guided him through speech and movement I learnt to communicate without fear. I began to understand emotion and how my behaviour can and does affect others. He allowed me to lie on his back he trusted me to not hurt him and I trusted him to care for me. I began to see a point in life and realise I had people who loved me and wanted to help me. Bruce taught me that through patience and gentleness I could succeed and fight my fears. He showed me that I could have a life.

Dear Jason

Jason, aged 22

I have chosen to write a letter to me aged 8 years because this is when I came into care. As an 8 year old I found it really scary to wake up, go downstairs and see my dad with a suitcase. I thought we were going on holiday but actually we were getting into a stranger's car (I did not know where we were going or what was going on) and then we pulled up outside someone's house then I remember going through the door with my parents and a suitcase and being told that I would have to stay here. I would not let go of my mum. I cried. I thought my mum and dad did not love me. Then they left.

Dear Jason (aged 8),

Things are going to be fine. Try not to worry or be afraid. You are going into a loving, warm family who will care for you. Eventually you will also see your old friends from primary school who you did not think you would see again. Bob and Mike will turn up and make you feel more at ease at your foster placement.

Life will be fine, there is light at the end of the tunnel.
Whenever you are offered help, accept that help.
Learn from your mistakes and be stronger.
Enjoy yourself; make new friends; you will be going to a new primary school literally down the road.
Have fun!!

My life

A, age 21

Your eye full of wonder, sparkling like the sun.
I didn't know how long I had to hold you. They were all
watching. I could almost read their doubtful minds that I
wouldn't be able to care for you. You was a miracle that took
over my life. Only I understand.

Without any fuss, you would not ask for much, a clean and feed,
no trouble as such. But I saw the need in your eyes, the need
for my love. That is when it struck, I couldn't give up. I held
your little fingers and made it my mission to get to the top, to
look on all of them doubtful minds and shut them all up! I felt
your trust in me, and knew you was my future. I stood by every
hardship you went through to survive, the injections and blood
tests, I couldn't bare see you cry, I had a fire light up burning me
inside. That is when I realised I feel 100 times more of everything
that you feel for me.

You fought for your life and I am so proud, I couldn't bear the
thoughts of you up in them clouds. I prayed and prayed so here
you are now. You are not so little anymore, you're a big girl now,
you help with chores and never get bored. You answer my phone
and never leave me alone. You cuddle me tight and give me a
fright, you make me laugh even in the bath. But its not all been
good for us, we have had our fair share of bad too. I am glad you
have been by my side supporting me. You are much wiser than
your years of four, you can do anything. . . life is an open door.
Life passes too quickly, leave no word unspoken, you are the
best gift I can ask for, you are perfect and bring me happiness
and so much more, seems like only yesterday you were in my
tummy. I love you more every day. I love you more than words
can say. MY LITTLE GIRL.

(Being a mum at 15 and having people overlook everything you do is not easy but I am proud of my little girl and myself for proving all those social workers wrong!)

The M word...

Chloe, age 21

I've always wanted a mum. The type of mum who paints your toes, who listens to your secrets and laughs at the latest gossip; you know, a movie mum. Tess in Freaky Friday, Leigh in The Blind Side, hell I would even settle for Mrs George from Mean Girls, weird boob job and all. I just wanted a mother I could call my own.

I thought of her often. I thought of what she would look like, how she would walk, how she would talk. What her dress sense would be. Then, I wondered what her favourite colour was; I wondered if she had any allergies, her favourite food, you know the silly things that make a person. I wondered if she wondered about me too.

Not having a mum, without starting a pity party, was hard. It wasn't the big things, like bras, periods and boyfriends that made it hard, it was the constant reminders of her absence, and absence that I couldn't explain nor comprehend. Yes, she left when I was a baby. No, she had never come back. No, I didn't know if she was ever going to come back. I'm not sure if she is dead or alive. Yes it makes me sad. No, I don't know what she looks like.

I have spent years crying for a woman I never knew. I spent hours wishing she were there. I fantasised about her. I hoped she would love me as much as I loved her. I hoped she would be proud of me. I planned our first conversation in my mind, over and over again.

It was a Thursday, late evening, when I got a call saying they had found her. After 17 years, the wait for Godot was over. She was, in fact, alive and well, living less than 20 minutes away. I felt in that moment the world stopped. I had never thought I would get the chance to meet her, now the chance arose and I had forgotten the conversation I had so carefully planned. I called my friend, we went to McDonalds and we ate 20 chicken nuggets in silence.

The day arrived; I was going to meet her, my mother. I had changed my outfit too many times to remember, debated if I had worn too much makeup, and worried if my hair would get frizzy. But, I felt prepared, I had been waiting years to meet her; I was ready, I had been ready for quite a while to think of it. This was my moment, to talk to her, to tell her how much she had missed, to show her I was something to be proud of, someone to be loved. I remember when she walked through the door. She had jet-black hair, pale skin and green eyes. I always pictured her to be blonde, with brown eyes and a lover of fake tan. She was far from the movie mother I had dreamt of, but nevertheless, there she was, my mother.

My palms were sweating, my heart was racing and I opened my mouth to pour out my heart. Silence. I couldn't speak, the tears slowly trickled down my face, and for the first time in my life I was speechless. I sat in silence while she lied and gave her excuses, ultimately; it was crack cocaine or me. What hurt most was that she didn't seem to regret what she done, the story she told was full of 'ifs' and 'buts'. I waited, stupidly, for her to say sorry, and that she loved me, just like I had planned, but she didn't.

I had put so much power into this woman, this mother of mine. There is not a day that goes by, that I do not think of her. I have no resentment for her and I wish her all the best, but to be honest, I am quite good at painting and I should probably cut down on the gossiping.

When a door closes, a better door opens

Jenn-T, age 18

I have suffered, I know what it feels like not having anything to
eat
I have suffered, only for great occasions my mother cooked meat
Not having enough, I used to go to school with broken shoes in
my feet
In my class everyone was rich, I had to work very hard to reserve
my seat

My mum sometimes cried when she looked at me
Saying I've got potential but will not find opportunity
It's not because she did not have big dreams for me
But because only money opens doors in my country

She stopped living her life just so I can live mine
She neglected herself for me but she didn't mind
Her love was overwhelming even though she couldn't provide
much
Even now after three years I can still feel her sweet touch

Our priority was my education
We couldn't afford to pay school but she had the determination.
Money wasn't bigger issue than my sexual orientation,
Which got me condemned by my entire nation.

Political issues where I come from created insecurity,
And it was not every day that my house had electricity.
I had to sleep in the dark despite my Achluophobia,
Gunshots every night were the reasons for my insomnia.

But with the help of the Lord I ended up coming to the UK
At first I had issues and things were not okay
Once I landed in the airport I was taken into care
Stopping me from realising my dream of living with my father
Living with strangers whilst my Dad has a house seemed a little unfair.
But I did not know that care would make my life even better.

But after all, since November last year,
I became independent I can buy what I want which makes me more confident.
I sleep peacefully and happily every night,
As there is no gunshots and I sleep with my light shine and bright.

I go to college gratuitously and I have other educational opportunities
I am celebrated at college for my achievement because I work to the best of my abilities
I can work part-time to provide to Mum and my family.
And I know one day I will give her life back to my Mummy

I am now free to be myself as my characteristics are protected.
But I could not where I come from or else I would have been killed
I work with **** City Council to make life better for the other kids.
Being involved as much as possible to help the council meeting their needs,
It is an opportunity for me to show my gratitude as ***** has changed my life
and life has changed my attitude

Being in the position that I am right now is a new beginning,
and this beginning is promising and wonderful
But I will always carry the memory of my past,
as it permits me to enjoy my new life and to be grateful.

Moving on

Shanika, age 12

The best thing about our experiences in life is that we always take something away from it, good or bad.
We learn from our mistakes, we laugh, live, learn and enjoy doing the things we love.
We learn to forgive and forget and that in time things get easier.
There have been many times when people have said 'things will heal in time' but because they have said that you try to hold on and think,
I'm not going to let that happen. Things do get easier as time goes on. You just have to let people in and learn to move on.
Moving on doesn't mean forgetting – because something or somebody you care about will always be a part of you no matter what – moving on means moving forwards – life goes on! And that is something I've had to learn.

Knowing that I'm part of a family is the best feeling in the world.
Knowing that somebody is always going to be there to support and stand by me has changed me forever.
I can't wait to make everyone proud.
I have become a different person this last year.

My abilities to laugh, to smile, to love, to trust have all been strengthened: strengthened enough to be able to guide me through the tough challenges that will be thrown at me in later life. Challenges I know I won't ever have to face alone.
Because I have a family.
A family isn't about DNA or your surname or anything like that.
It doesn't matter what comes in front of the word family, in my case foster, it's the love and consideration to each one of their hearts; which is what makes my family so good.

And if it weren't for my foster parents, the two most incredible and loving people I've ever met, I wouldn't have had the amazing experience of being part of a family!